3 Write as semibreves (whole notes) the scales named below.

E minor, descending, with key signature.

Which form of the minor scale have you used? ....

E♭ major, ascending, without key signature but adding any necessary sharp or flat signs.

4 Rewrite the following in notes of *half* the value, beginning as shown.
Remember to group (beam) the notes correctly where necessary.

O. Lassus

5 Write the tonic triads named below. Do *not* use key signatures, but remember to add any necessary sharp or flat signs.

      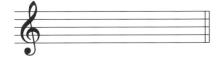

Bb major   A minor   G major

D minor   D major

6 Add the correct rest(s) at the places marked ∗ in these two melodies to make each bar complete.

Naudot

Berlioz

7 (a) Name the degree of the scale (e.g. 2nd, 3rd) of each of the notes marked ∗, as shown in the first answer. The key is B♭ major.

2nd   ....

(b) Draw a circle around a note in this melody that is *not* in the key of B♭ major.

8 Look at this melody by Smetana and then answer the questions below.

Write your answer to question (c) on the stave below.

(a) Give the meaning of each of these:

vivace ....

♩=72 ....

mf ....

the dots above the notes (e.g. bar 3) ....

:‖ (bar 8) ....

〔10〕

(b) (i) Name the degree of the scale (e.g. 2nd, 3rd)
of the *first* note in the melody. The key is A major. ....

(ii) Complete this sentence:
Bar 2 has the same notes and rhythm as bar ....

(iii) How many semiquavers (16th notes)
are the tied notes in bars 4–5 worth in total? ....

(iv) Draw a circle around two notes next to each other that are a 5th apart.

(v) Complete this sentence: The **4** in **2/4** means ....

〔10〕

(c) Copy out the music from the start of bar 5 to the end of the melody, exactly as it is
written above. Don't forget the clef, key signature, dynamics and all other details.
Write the music on the blank stave above question (a).
(Marks will be given for neatness and accuracy.)

〔10〕

Theory Paper Grade 2   2011   B

Duration 1½ hours

TOTAL MARKS
100

Candidates should answer ALL questions.
Write your answers on this paper – no others will be accepted.
Answers must be written clearly and neatly – otherwise marks may be lost.

1 Add the time signature to each of these five melodies.

10

2 Write a four-bar rhythm using the given opening.

10

3 (a) Rewrite these treble clef notes in the bass clef, keeping the pitch the same.
The first answer is given.

(b) In which major key are all these notes found? ....

4 Add the correct clef and any necessary sharp or flat signs to make each of the scales named below. Do *not* use key signatures.

A minor

Which form of the minor scale have you used? ....

D major

5 *After* each note write a *higher* note to form the named *melodic* interval, as shown in the first answer. The key is G major.

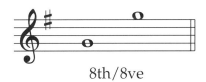      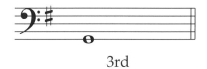

   8th/8ve   5th   3rd

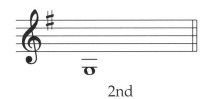   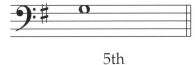   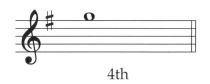

   2nd   7th   4th

6 Rewrite this melody *without* using a key signature. Remember to include sharp, flat or natural signs where they are needed. The key is A major and the first four notes are given.

Mozart

7 Add the correct clef to make each of these named notes, as shown in the first answer.

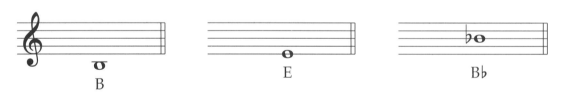

B

E

B♭

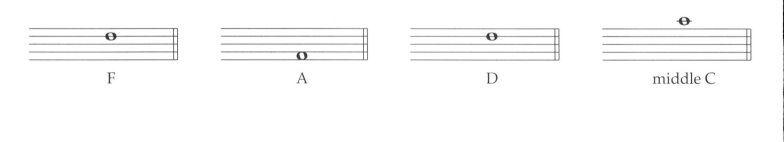

F

A

D

middle C

C♯

G

F♯

D

8 Look at this melody by Mendelssohn and then answer the questions below.

Write your answer to question (c) on the stave below.

(a) Give the meaning of each of these:

lento ....

mf ....

cantabile ....

⸺ (e.g. bar 4) ....

sf (bar 5) ....

(b) (i) This melody is in the key of F major. Draw a circle around two notes next to each other that are a 6th apart.

10

(ii) Give the letter name of the first note in bar 7. ....

(iii) Give the time name (e.g. crotchet or quarter note) of the *shortest* note in the melody. ....

(iv) Name the degree of the scale (e.g. 2nd, 3rd) of the *last* note in the melody (marked *). Remember the key is F major. ....

(v) Underline one of the following words that best describes how you think bar 7 of this melody should be played:

legato (smoothly) or *staccato* (detached)

(c) Copy out the music from the start of bar 5 to the end of the melody, exactly as it is written above. Don't forget the clef, key signature, dynamics and all other details. Write the music on the blank stave above question (a).
(Marks will be given for neatness and accuracy.)

10

Theory Paper Grade 2   2011   C

Duration 1½ hours

Candidates should answer ALL questions.
Write your answers on this paper – no others will be accepted.
Answers must be written clearly and neatly – otherwise marks may be lost.

TOTAL MARKS
100

1 Add the missing bar-lines to these two melodies. The first bar-line is given in each.

10

2 Write a four-bar rhythm using the given opening.

10

3 Rewrite this melody in the treble clef, keeping the pitch the same.
   The first two notes are given.

10

4 Write as semibreves (whole notes) the scales named below.   10

E minor, descending, with key signature.

Which form of the minor scale have you used? ....

B♭ major, ascending, without key signature but adding any necessary sharp or flat signs.

5 Give the number (e.g. 2nd, 3rd) of each of these melodic intervals, as shown in the first   10
answer. The key is A major.

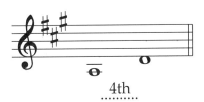

4th
....

....

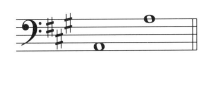

....

....

....

....

6 Rewrite the following melody, grouping (beaming) the notes in bars 1–3 correctly.

Chopin

7 (a) Name the degree of the scale (e.g. 2nd, 3rd) of each of the notes marked ∗, as shown in the first answer. The key is E♭ major.

Schumann

7th

(b) Give the letter name of the *last* note in bar 1. ....

8 Look at this melody by Grieg and then answer the questions below.

Write your answer to question (c) on the stave below.

(a) Give the meaning of each of these: [10]

Poco ....

andante ....

♩=66 ....

pp ....

cresc. (bar 5) ....

(b) (i) Underline one of the following words that best describes how you think   [10]
bars 1–4 of this melody should be played:

legato (smoothly)   or   *staccato* (detached)

(ii) This melody is in the key of A minor.
Draw a circle around a note that is *not* in this key.

(iii) Which other key has the same key signature as A minor? ....

(iv) Give the number of a bar that contains
all the notes of the tonic triad of A minor. Bar ....

(v) How many times does the rhythm  occur? ....

(c) Copy out the music from the start of the melody to the end of bar 4, exactly as it is   [10]
written above. Don't forget the clef, time signature, tempo marking, dynamic and
all other details. Write the music on the blank stave above question (a).
(Marks will be given for neatness and accuracy.)

Theory Paper Grade 2   2011   S

Duration 1½ hours

Candidates should answer ALL questions.
Write your answers on this paper – no others will be accepted.
Answers must be written clearly and neatly – otherwise marks may be lost.

TOTAL MARKS
100

1   Add the missing bar-lines to these two melodies. The first bar-line is given in each.

10

Schumann

Berlioz

2   Write a four-bar rhythm using the given opening.

10

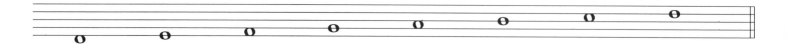

3   Add the correct clef and any necessary sharp or flat signs to make each of the scales named below. Do *not* use key signatures.

10

D minor

Which form of the minor scale have you used? ....

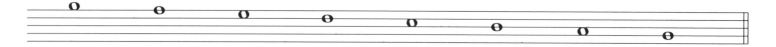

B♭ major

4 (a) Give the letter name of each of the notes marked ∗, including the sharp or flat sign where necessary. The first answer is given. `10`

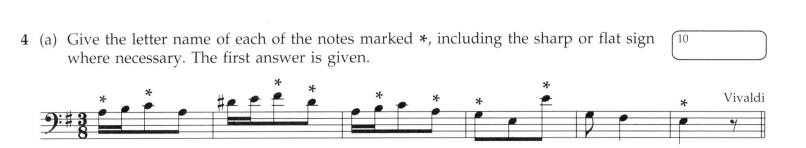

A
....

(b) How many times does the rhythm  occur? ....

5 Name the keys of these tonic triads. `10`

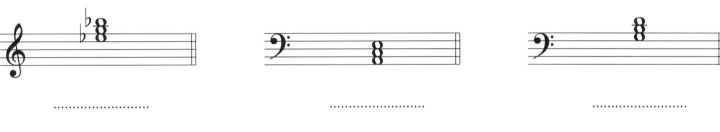

....

....

6 Rewrite this melody in the bass clef, keeping the pitch the same. The first bar is given. `10`

Spontini

7 Add the correct rest(s) at the places marked ∗ in these two melodies to make each bar complete. `10`

Grieg

F. Halévy

8 Look at this melody by Mozart and then answer the questions below.

Write your answer to question (c) on the stave below.

(a) Give the meaning of each of these: [10]

Andante ....

p (e.g. bar 1) ....

⌢ (e.g. bar 3) ....

f (bar 6) ....

the dots above the notes (e.g. bar 10) ....

(b) (i) Complete this sentence: [10]
The **8** in **⅜** means ....

   (ii) Answer TRUE OR FALSE to this sentence:
The tied notes in bars 1–2 are worth 10 semiquavers (16th notes) in total. ....

   (iii) Give the time name (e.g. crotchet or
quarter note) of the rest in the *last* bar of this melody. ....

   (iv) Name the degree of the scale (e.g. 4th, 5th)
of the *last* note in the melody. The key is C major. ....

   (v) Draw a circle around two notes next to each other that are a 4th apart.

(c) Copy out the music from the start of the melody to the end of bar 6, exactly as it is [10]
written above. Don't forget the clef, time signature, tempo marking, dynamics and
and all other details. Write the music on the blank stave above question (a).
(Marks will be given for neatness and accuracy.)

ABRSM
24 Portland Place
London W1B 1LU
United Kingdom

www.abrsm.org

Theory of Music Exams Model An
are also available.

Published by ABRSM (Publishing) Ltd,
a wholly owned subsidiary of ABRSM

Printed in England by Page Bros (Norwic

SCHOTT MUSIC
ABRSM / Theory Exam Pap

9781848493681

Location:

ONo.:9781848493681

£ 2.75